This Too Shall Pass: Turning Pain Into Power

A Healing Journal for the Woman Needing Encouragement After A Miscarriage

Simbi M. Animashaun

1

This Too Shall Pass: Turning Pain Into Power

A Healing Journal for the Woman Needing Encouragement After A Miscarriage

For more information on upcoming events, visit my website
https://simbianimashaun.com

Table of Contents

Acknowledgment

I am humbled by God's grace and mercy towards me. I thank him for allowing me to share his magnificent work again. My first published book, *The Power of Healing: A Memoir of Loss & Victory*, has received great reviews and touched many women's lives across the country.

Since its release, I have been invited to be guest speakers at women's empowerment events, and I have even donated my book to women who have recently suffered pregnancy or child loss and seek healing and encouragement.

I am finally fulfilling my purpose in life, and I owe it all to God. Likewise, I struggled for years with pregnancy loss (i.e., miscarriages), but he showed me the power of healing. Now, I share my story with others, with hopes of inspiring them. Finally, I thank God for entrusting me to create a healing journal to accompany my book.

I also thank my three children for giving me hope and inspiration each day. They are daily reminders of how magnificent God is. My life would be entirely different if they did not exist.

Lastly, I thank my family and friends who have consistently supported me and my new role as a published author and mompreneur. It takes a village, and occasionally, it is hard to create that village when everyone is consumed with their lives.

My oldest son was diagnosed with Autism Spectrum Disorder (ASD) in January 2021. Since his diagnosis, his special education preschool teacher (Ms. Gonzalez) has been by my side reassuring me that things would be alright.

She not only offered her love and support for my son, but for all of my children. I have a few other friends, who made promises and kept them. I appreciate the ones who have been there for my children and me.

Moreover, I know life happens, and I do not fault anyone for missing an event or not calling to check on the well-being of the children and me. I understand. I pray that God allows you to be at peace soon.

To end, whenever I felt like giving up, I could also always count on my grandmother to get me back on track. She has never left my side, and I am thankful God placed her in my life.

Introduction

A miscarriage is lonely, painful, and depressing. Michelle Obama writes in her memoir *Becoming* (2018), *If I were to create a file on things no one tells you about until you're right in the middle of them, I might start with miscarriages.*

When you have experienced one, you will probably think it is a personal failing, but it is not. The agony of a miscarriage is indescribable. I suffered in silence for over 10 years because I was afraid of how the world would view me. I was afraid of being judged by my family, friends, and even strangers.

10

Everyone thought I was this STRONG woman who had her life in order. I did, but partially. I am a work in progress. Not only that, but I am not perfect. I am human.

I refused to be like many of my family members, so I worked hard in school to be great! However, I did not always make the best decisions; I had no guidance or role models besides my grandmother. I could have excelled to higher levels, but we are products of our environments. I became that at an early age.

By age 16, I was living an adult life: drinking, smoking, partying, skipping school, staying out late, disrespecting my grandmother, and being promiscuous. It is not the life I wanted to live: I felt like I did not have a choice. It was the only way to fit in with my peers and survive in my neighborhood.

I had to grow up fast. I did not have a chance to enjoy my childhood. To this day, I hardly remember any memorable experiences of my family. Memory loss may contribute to the brain hemorrhage I suffered in November 2014, but I always ask for pictures, and there are hardly any in my family.

As a child, I witnessed and experienced situations that left me traumatized. It left me hardened and broken. At the age of 10, I witnessed my mother almost dying after getting shot five times by her boyfriend. I never had a father figure growing up, and I always wondered why. I had a living father, but he stopped visiting or contributing to my well-being before my mother's near-death experience.

Life happens, and you eventually forget about the people who are not active in your life. During that horrifying time, my father was still absent. No one in my family, including my mother, thought it was important to take me to see a therapist after everything that I had experienced. I needed it. I just did not know how to express it to anyone.

To be honest, I did not know the purpose of counseling. I just knew my school had counselors who I could talk to if I encountered any problems. But, I never did!

During my teenage years, I discovered a way to mask the childhood trauma, insecurities, and anxiety that I had endured. I tried to fit in with my peers, but it was difficult to establish genuine friendships and relationships when no one understood me or my past. I also chose to date the wrong men who left me heartbroken.

Furthermore, I held a lot of my pain inside. I just wanted to be loved, but I later discovered the secret to love: I needed to love myself first. When I began to experience repeated trauma as an adult, I decided to change the narrative.

I found a solution to my brokenness. God! My faith became strong, during all the times I spent alone, in the hospital, at home, in my bedroom, etc. I hoped that my family and friends would come to rescue me.

No one did, so I had to stop being of this world and connect with God. When I did, my life changed forever. He started removing people from my life who were distractions and started connecting me with people who genuinely cared about me and my future.

After sharing my testimony about my struggle with miscarriages and my journey to motherhood in my first published book, *The Power of Healing: A Memoir of Loss & Victory*, I am inspired to create a healing journal that will help other women grieve from their losses (in particularly pregnancy and infant) and turn the pain into POWER!

I am 1 in 4! I understand the damage that is done when a pregnancy ends unexpectedly as a miscarriage or a baby is born silent. It hurts! It hurts like hell. I experienced my first miscarriage in 2014 while I was teaching my students. It was my first pregnancy, and I was pleased to finally become a mother. I was hurt, devastated, and embarrassed.

After I had the miscarriage, I never told anyone except for the baby's father. Miscarriage is a lonely place. I experienced three more miscarriages within the next two years.

My pain turned into power when I decided to stop blaming God and began the healing process. The purpose of this healing journal, *This Too Shall Pass: Turning Pain Into*

Power, is to provide 7 steps to turning your pain into power after you have experienced pregnancy loss.

I also want to raise awareness of pregnancy and infant loss. This experience is nothing to be ashamed of. A miscarriage is a regular occurrence. More women have probably lost a child to this world than have not. Most people do not talk about it and continue about their lives as if it never happened.

I am not a medical expert or trained therapist, but I have firsthand experienced recurrent miscarriages. I know how it feels after the loss. In this journal, I will take you on the journey I took when healing from my miscarriages and openly share the tools and resources that I used to heal.

You may not feel comfortable speaking about your loss to others yet, but please do not hold it in. Use this journal to be vulnerable. To share your thoughts and feelings. To emotionally heal. At the end of each chapter, I offer a special prayer for you. *This Too Shall Pass*! Do not be ashamed of your story. It will inspire others.

Step 1: You Are Not On Your Own

"Give all your worries and cares to God, for he cares about you." 1 Peter 5:7

For most women, when we discover that we are pregnant, it is the happiest moment ever. When I discovered that I was pregnant in 2014, I was in disbelief, but I was also filled with so much joy. Before meeting my kid's father, I had dated a man for nearly ten years. We met during my sophomore year in college.

After we both graduated from college and moved to Maryland to start our careers, I began to express that I wanted kids, but he made sure he expressed clearly that he did not.

Although he was five years older, he was afraid of living life, getting married, or starting a family. I do not fault him for the time wasted; we all have demons that we are fighting and trying to overcome. To this day, I am unsure what his issues were; he was raised in a household with a mother and father. Again, I do not know what his issues were.

At the end of our relationship, I met a new guy through a friend. After seven months, I became pregnant, but I did not find out until I tried to do everything right, regarding eating, exercising, sleeping, and keeping my stress levels low. I was teaching 8th grade English Language Arts (ELA) at the time. Unfortunately, my pregnancy ended in a miscarriage eight weeks later.

To make matters worse, it happened unexpectedly while I was giving directions to my students. Luckily, they did not notice what I was experiencing at that time. I quickly ran out of the school building and drove myself to the nearest emergency room.

After bleeding on myself for nearly an hour and being forced to undergo a bloody ultrasound, the doctor entered the room and said the most terrifying words to me:

"The baby did not have a heartbeat. I am sorry, Ms. Animashaun."

I would hear those terrifying words three more times within the next two years.

I had a total of FOUR miscarriages. Although I went on to have three beautiful children, it still hurts, and I always think about my children who did not make it. *YOU ARE NOT ON YOUR OWN*!

I. **Process**

You may have experienced pregnancy or child loss today, yesterday, or even a month ago. Regardless of the date, there is no expiration date on healing. I am still hurt by the loss of pregnancies, but I am now open to sharing my story with others.

II. Reflection

Share your story. What happened? How do you feel about your loss? Was it your first pregnancy? First child?

I got pregnant Jan 2021 - I was so excited, this would of been the 1st child for my BF - I bled the whole time, thought something was wrong. April 2021 I went in for my ultrasound. BF on the Phone. We were told there Was No Heartbeat. Angel Due Date was October 2021. Fast Foward to 2022 -

Pregnant Feb 2022 - Went into early labor in - 21 weeks later - we lost our Daughter Hope! This was my world crashing

III. Research

Surviving a miscarriage can be extremely painful. As your body recovers from a miscarriage, you could endure a roller coaster of emotions as well as physical symptoms. Physically, it takes a few weeks to a month or more to recuperate from a miscarriage. The length of your recuperation will be determined by how far along you were

26

in your pregnancy (American Pregnancy
Association, 2018).

I made the mistake of not telling anyone
about my losses, except for the baby's father.
I did not expect him to understand, though.
If I could go back in time, I would have
contacted my best friend at the time and
shared the bad news with her. Even though
she may not have known the "right" words to
say, I know she would have been there
"physically for me.

IV. Reflection

Is there anyone, besides the baby's father
(e.g., best friend, mother, grandmother,

colleague, sister, etc.), with whom you can share your loss? If so, who would it be and why?

NO Body !.

Sometimes my Daughter she is Amazing.

Not MY Daughter Father Not Friends / Family

Prayer

God, please send me some words of encouragement to help me get through this difficult time of losing my baby. I am counting on you to guide me through this darkness so that I can find your light. I am stuck in a hole of pain and misery, and I need you. You are the only one who can get me through this. Please assist. Amen.

Step 2: Self-Care Is Important

"I have told you these things, so that in me, you may have peace. In this world, you will have trouble. But take heart! I have overcome the world."

John 16:33

When I was discharged from the hospital the day I had my first miscarriage, I immediately went home and stayed in my bed for days. I was hurt. Broken. I had no one to talk to, or perhaps I did, but I was too embarrassed and ashamed to contact my family and friends to inform them of my loss.

I buried myself in tears and began questioning God. *Why me, Lord?* I asked repeatedly. My days and nights turned into guilt. I started to blame myself for the miscarriage. Amid the blame, I began to neglect myself. I stopped socializing with my family and friends. I stopped eating right and exercising. Furthermore, I began to drink heavily, depending on alcohol to make the pain go away. Not only that, but I was heartbroken.

But, life changed for me a few months later. After visiting my gynecologist, she shared with me the possibility of getting pregnant again. Chances were high, and if I wanted to have a successful future pregnancy, I needed to focus on self-care.

I learned that even though the pregnancy may not have continued, caring for my body was important to my miscarriage recovery.

From that moment, I started my miscarriage recovery. I was still emotionally hurt by my loss; I just wanted something relaxing to do. I located a massage salon and scheduled quarterly therapeutic postnatal massages.

Luckily, it was covered by my health insurance plan. After a year, I started to feel like myself again. I started to live my regular life: traveling, shopping, hanging out with my friends, etc.

I. **Process**

Healing is a process, so please do not think that you will be over your loss tomorrow or next week. Healing may take months or years. Body healing is aided by hydration, healthy nourishment, mild activity, and sleep.

Consider trying a new physical activity, such as cycling, boxing, or that provides you joy or allows you to express yourself emotionally. If at all feasible, this is an excellent time to spend more time on self-care than usual.

Self-care allowed me to shift my focus from my loss to the possibility of new beginnings. The goal is not to forget about your loss. The goal is to heal from your loss so that you can have a fulfilling life.

II. Research

According to the American Pregnancy Association (2012), Although there is no ideal period to wait before trying to conceive again, many healthcare experts advise women to wait at least a few months to increase their chances of a healthy pregnancy.

If a woman's body is not ready to maintain a pregnancy by the time she conceives again, she'll have a higher chance of having another miscarriage. It takes time for the uterus to repair and the endometrial lining to re-establish its strength and health.

According to Johns Hopkins Medicine (n.d.) When a set of blood arteries in your body forms wrongly, AVMs occur. Arteries and veins get unusually knotted and create direct connections, bypassing normal tissues, in these abnormalities. This usually happens before or shortly after birth, during development.

The majority of persons with AVMs have no symptoms or issues at first. Instead, the issue is identified when doctors are treating another, unrelated health issue. A rupture of one of the blood arteries in an AVM can sometimes bring the problem to medical

_____

_____

_____

_____

_____

_____

_____

_____

_____

_____

Prayer
*God, please look after my darling child.
Please help me to have patience and
endurance till I reach Heaven and meet my
lovely child.
Thank you for reminding me that this is
simply the beginning of our journey together
in Heaven. Amen.*

Step 6: Memorialize the Baby

"The LORD gave, and the LORD has taken away; may the name of the LORD be praised." Job 1:21b

Before I found out I was pregnant with my daughter in 2019, I randomly went to the nearest tattoo parlor in my neighborhood and got a tattoo to honor and memorialize my babies. It is permanent and will remain with me always- never forgetting my journey to motherhood.

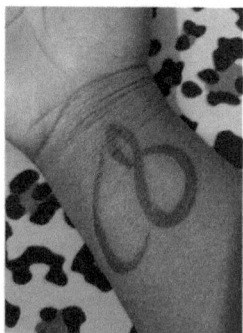 After I published my first book, *The Power of Healing: A Memoir of Loss & Victory in* May 2021, I began to meet other women who were inspired by my story. They may have endured

pregnancy or infant loss themselves or known a family or close friend who did. It seemed like more and more women started to share their stories as well.

One day on my way to taking my daughter to her parent & tot gymnastics class, an idea popped into my head. I thought it would be awesome to plan and host a remembrance event in the Atlanta area on Pregnancy & Infant Loss Awareness Day on October 15.

When I presented the idea to my sorority sister (*we're members of the illustrious Alpha Kappa Alpha Sorority, Inc.*) and my peers in a

Facebook post, I received an overwhelming amount of praise and acceptance to attend.

In that post, both men and women shared their losses. It was surprisingly shocking because I had never heard men state that they too had experienced a miscarriage.

Most men are not emotionally impacted by this ordeal, but they should be because those were their babies too. I researched several ways to memorialize our babies. There are tons of ideas available on Instagram, Facebook, Pinterest, etc. For my event, we are going to gather and release balloons in honor of all of our babies in heaven.

I. Process

A miscarriage can feel like the loss of a child for many couples. Recognizing your pregnancy loss in a meaningful way can be a healthy and appropriate way to grieve.

Here are <u>five ways</u> to honor your baby after miscarriage or infant loss and help with the healing process:

1. **Tree Planting**- You can choose a tree that symbolizes the baby's birth month or a tree that blooms in a color you have chosen for them.

2. **Balloon Release**- It is a beautiful ceremony to remember babies who passed. Pick colors that are special to you. You can even write the baby's name on the balloon before releasing it.

3. **Give Your Baby A Name**- Naming your baby after a miscarriage is an amazing way to honor your baby.

4. **Jewelry**- You can get your baby's name engraved into a piece of jewelry (e.g., rings, necklaces, and bracelets). You can also use gems and charms to memorialize your baby.

5. **Shadow Box or Keepsake Box-**
Keeping things like ultrasound pictures, hospital bracelets, blankets, positive pregnancy tests, and clothing will allow you to memorialize your baby.

II. Reflection

After reading this section, how do you plan to memorialize your baby? How often will you honor your baby? Will you include family and friends? If so, who do you plan to include? Why?

_____

_____

without even trying to know your story, so it is best to live your life for YOU. Not THEM!

After everything I had endured: miscarriages, heartbreak, a brain hemorrhage, etc., some people still decided to judge my situation for having children back-to-back. However, by this point in my life, I do not care what others have to say or what they think of me. The only judgment I care about is the one from God. When I was losing children or even endured that near-death experience, I can only remember 1-2 people being there for me.

I. **Process**

I realized that the only person I could truly depend on was God, I changed my mindset. Immediately, my life began to change. I began to grow as a woman, mother, friend, and in my professional career as a teacher.

The pain that I carried for over five years had turned into POWER! I do not mean that in a conceited manner. Someone with power has physical strength or is in command of a situation. I am in control of my thoughts and actions. At all times, I try to be and surround myself with positive energy.

My newfound power allowed me to break free from the negative thoughts in my mind. I

_____

_____

_____

_____

_____

_____

_____

_____

Prayer

God, I cannot believe how much sadness I feel for someone I have never met. It is strange to lose a child who has not yet been born. While the sensation is unusual, the pain is the same since I am their mother and they will always be my child, whether I met them or not. Please, God, grant me healing and blessings as a result of this. Amen.

story of pregnancy loss with others. Her social media platform regularly addresses her struggle with pregnancy loss. She is a member of many support groups, both formally and informally.

Helpful Websites & Books

- Parents or other family members who have lost a baby between conception and the first month of life can request a free March of Dimes bereavement kit by calling 1-800-367-6630 or emailing bkit@marchofdimes.org.
- Other Helpful Websites:
  - www.mend.org
  - www.thelifeididntchoose.com
  - www.babyloss.com
  - [www.miscarriagesupport.ohttps://www.mother.ly/life/i-had-a-miscarriagerg.nz](https://www.mother.ly/life/i-had-a-miscarriage)
- Helpful Books:
  - The Power of Healing: A Memoir of Loss & Victory - by Simbi M. Animashaun
  - Miscarriage: Women Sharing from the Heart — by Shelly Marks, Marie Allen
  - Miscarriage: A Shattered Dream — by Sherokee Isle, Linda Hammer Burns

- Surviving Pregnancy Loss: A complete sourcebook for women and their families — by Rochelle Friedman and Bonnie Gradstein
- I Had a Miscarriage: A Memoir, A Movement by Jessica Zucker

References

American Pregnancy Association (2012). Pregnancy after miscarriage. Retrieved from https://americanpregnancy.org/getting-pregnant/pregnancy-loss/pregnancy-after-miscarriage-71034/

American Pregnancy Association (2017). After a miscarriage. Retrieved from https://americanpregnancy.org/getting-pregnant/pregnancy-loss/physical-recovery-after-miscarriage-71059/

American Pregnancy Association (2020). After a miscarriage: Surviving emotionally. Retrieved from https://americanpregnancy.org/getting-pregnant/pregnancy-loss/miscarriage-surviving-emotionally-582/

John Hopkins Medicine (n.d.). Arteriovenous malfunction. Retrieved from https://www.hopkinsmedicine.org/health/conditions-and-diseases/arteriovenous-malformations#:~:text=Arteriovenous%20malformations%20(AVMs)%20happen%20when,before%20birth%20or%20shortly%20after

Mayo Clinic (n.d.). Polycystic ovary syndrome (PCOS). Retrieved from https://www.mayoclinic.org/diseases-conditions/pcos/symptoms-causes/syc-20353439#:~:text=Polycystic%20ovary%20syndrome%20(PCOS)%20is,fail%20to%20regularly%20release%20eggs

Miscarriage Association (n.d.). A nurse's view. Retrieved from https://www.miscarriageassociation.org.uk/your-feelings/pregnancyaftermiscarriage/pregnancy-miscarriage-nurses-view/